Ranger Ron to the Rescue

by David Leverett

 For my grandchildren Alex and Zoe Leverett

Ranger Ron to the Rescue

The stormy night, with its strong winds and pouring rain, has passed over. The morning starts calm and sunny.

Ranger Ron decides to leave for work early, as he wants to see what damage has been caused by the storm. He is the Park Ranger and he looks after the lake, the river, the trees and the flowers. He makes sure that the birds, the animals and the fish are always safe and well.

'Have a nice day,' says his wife Sara, as he sets off with his lunch box and his mobile phone, ready for the day ahead.

1

Ranger Ron has a meeting in the conservatory with his trainee, Ali, to discuss which urgent jobs need to be done.

They decide that Ali will check for damage to buildings, play area equipment and trees. Ron will make sure no birds or animals are hurt or stranded.

They are very pleased to see that the conservatory has not been damaged by the storm, so they each have a mug of tea before they set off to do their work.

Before he leaves, Ron contacts Jill Jones, the vet, on his mobile phone. He tells her that he may need her help later in the day.

Ranger Ron's first job is to rescue a family of rabbits, made homeless when the great oak blew down in the storm. It destroyed their burrow, which was deep in the roots of the tree.

A grey squirrel and a blackbird have also lost their nests, high in the branches. So Ron helps them too.

Follow Ranger Ron to the Rescue around the park.

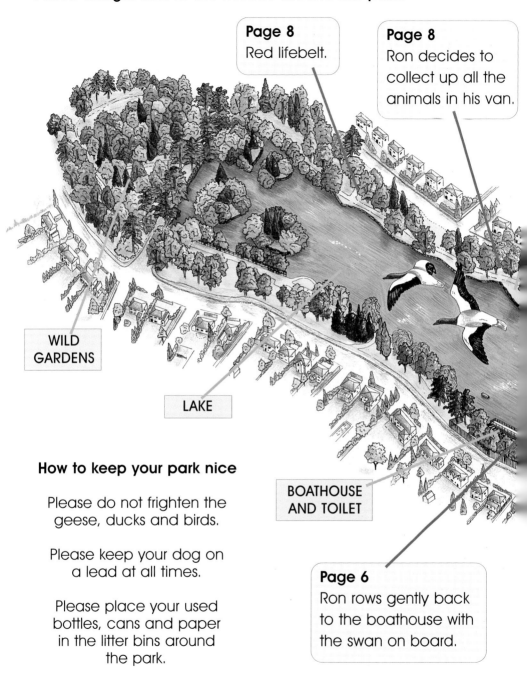

Page 8
Red lifebelt.

Page 8
Ron decides to collect up all the animals in his van.

WILD GARDENS

LAKE

BOATHOUSE AND TOILET

How to keep your park nice

Please do not frighten the geese, ducks and birds.

Please keep your dog on a lead at all times.

Please place your used bottles, cans and paper in the litter bins around the park.

Page 6
Ron rows gently back to the boathouse with the swan on board.

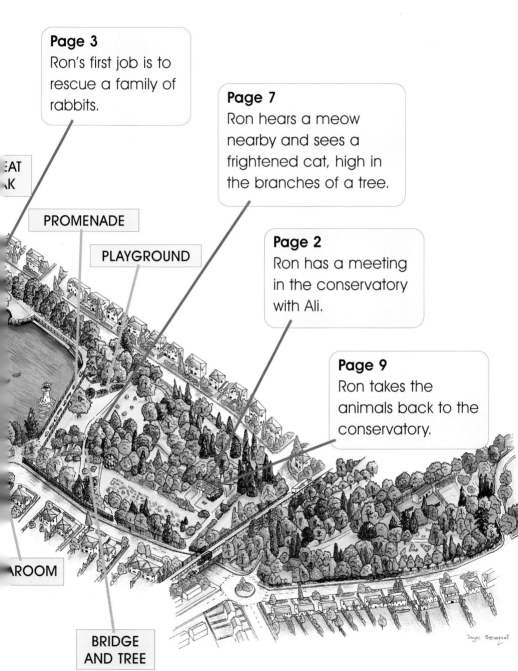

Page 3
Ron's first job is to rescue a family of rabbits.

Page 7
Ron hears a meow nearby and sees a frightened cat, high in the branches of a tree.

Page 2
Ron has a meeting in the conservatory with Ali.

Page 9
Ron takes the animals back to the conservatory.

EAT
K

PROMENADE

PLAYGROUND

ROOM

BRIDGE AND TREE

A lady walking her dog around the lake tells Ranger Ron she has seen a swan in pain. She says it has a fishing line and hook caught in its beak.

Ron thanks the lady and goes to fetch his rowing boat. He paddles out to the injured swan. All the birds and animals in the park trust him, so he is able to get the swan into the boat.

Ron rows gently back to the boathouse with the swan on board and contacts the vet. He arranges for her to come over to remove the hook from the swan's beak.

Ranger Ron hears a meow nearby and sees a frightened cat, high in the branches of a beech tree.

It is so high off the ground that he has to fetch an extending ladder. He can only just reach the cold and hungry animal.

After a few kind words from Ron, the cat soon comes to him and he takes it down. It runs off home to a nearby house.

Many different animals have been frightened away from their homes by the storm, so Ranger Ron decides to collect them all up in his van. He decides to take them back to the conservatory, where they can be fed and checked over by Jill Jones, the vet.

So he drives slowly around the park and picks up a fox, a badger, some hedgehogs, some squirrels and some rabbits. He even picks up a grass snake! He finds it curled up under the branch of a fallen tree and he knows it's harmless.

With all the animals fed and checked, Ali has a good idea. 'Before we release them back into the wild, why don't we put on a free Wildlife Show? We can let children see live animals up close, instead of just on television or in books.'

'Great,' says Jill, 'and I can give them a little talk about how we must be kind to all animals and birds.'

So the day ended very happily for Ranger Ron and all his friends.

Vocabulary

Page 1

rescue	-	to take away from danger
calm	-	quiet, no wind
damage	-	to break, spoil
caused	-	made to happen

Page 2

conservatory	-	glass building used to grow rare plants
trainee	-	person learning to do a job
equipment	-	swings, slides and climbing frames
vet	-	animal and bird doctor

Page 3

destroyed	-	broken so badly it cannot be used again
burrow	-	underground tunnel dug by animals

Page 4

paddling	-	using oars in water to move a boat
injured	-	hurt part of the body
boathouse	-	building used to store boats

Page 5

extending	-	made longer
nearby	-	close to

Page 6

collect	-	pick up and gather together
checked	-	looked at closely

Page 7

release	-	to set free